Get Set Go!

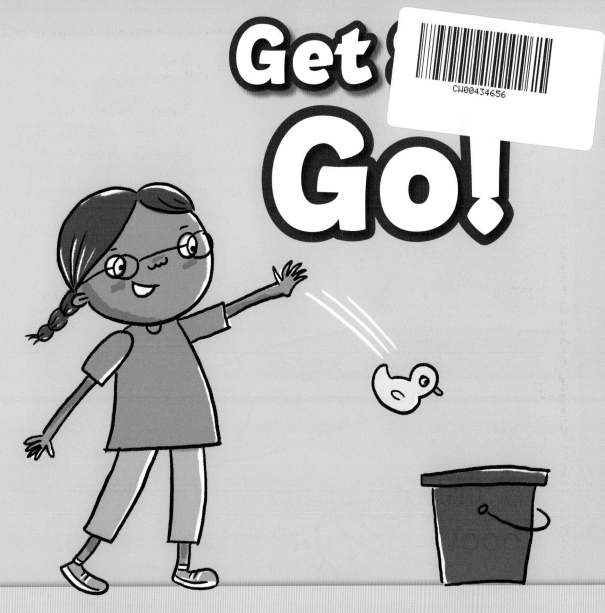

Written by Fiona Undrill
Illustrated by Hannah Wood

Map

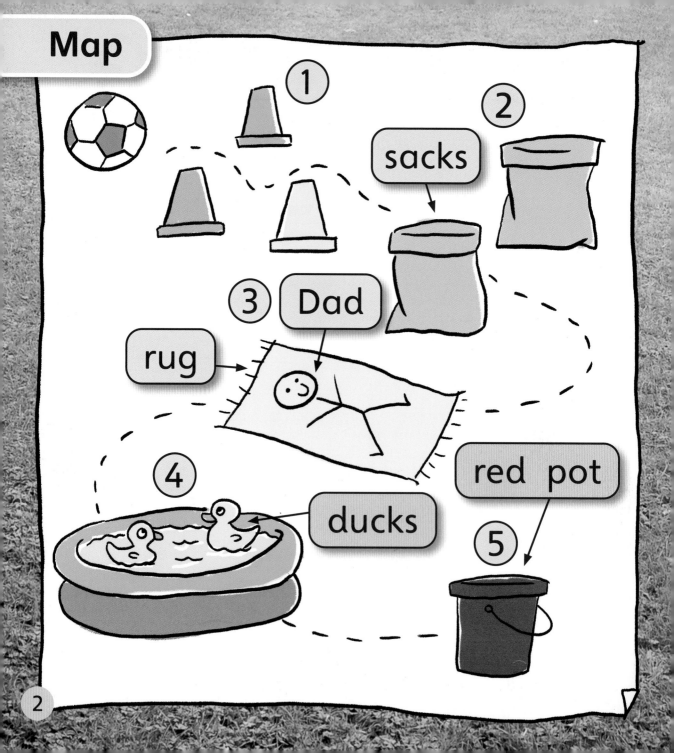

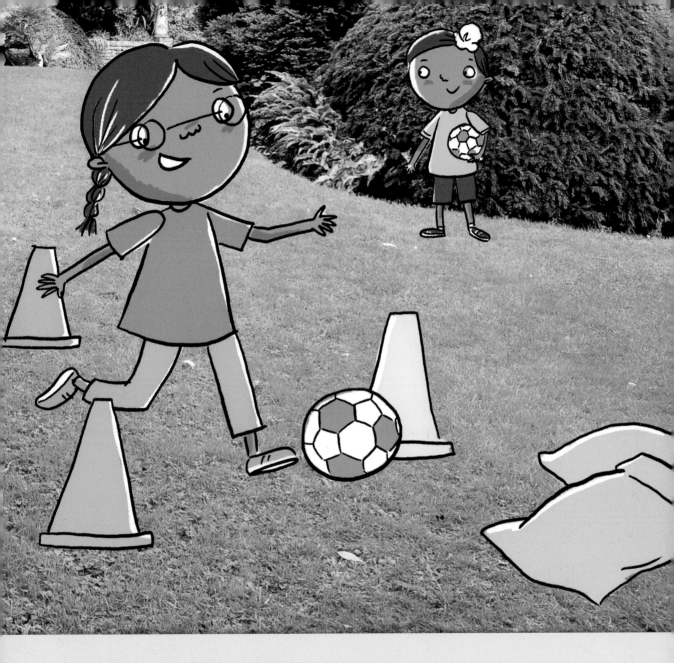

1 Kick to the sacks.

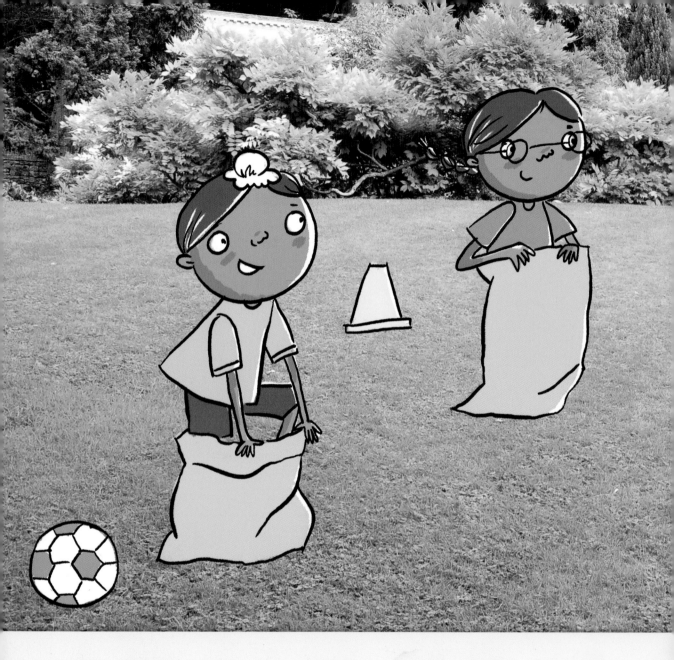

2 Pick up a sack and get in it.

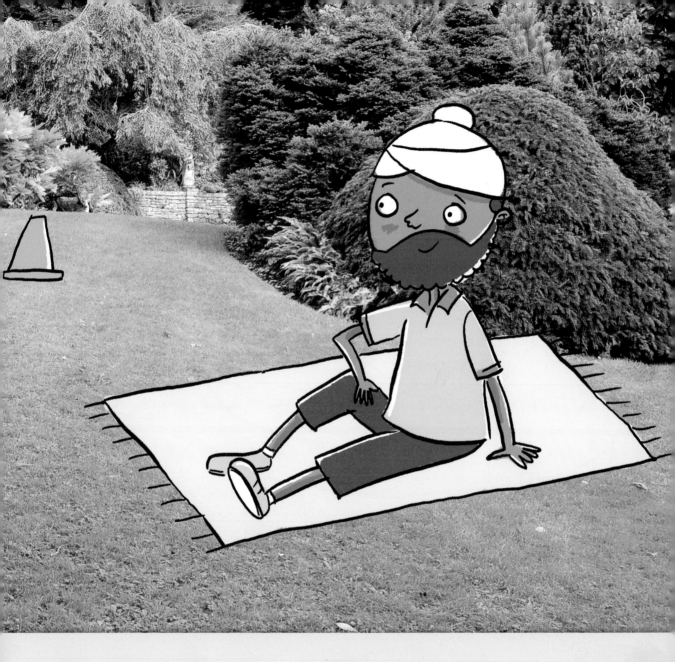

3 Go to the rug.

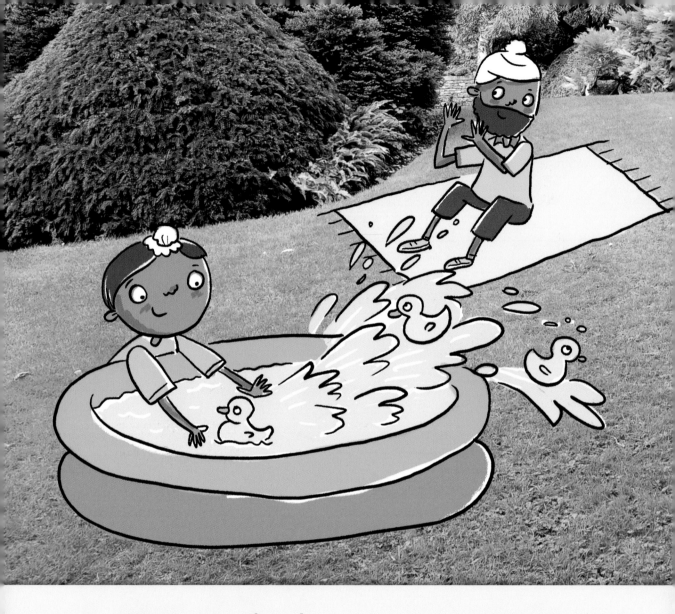

4 Get a duck.

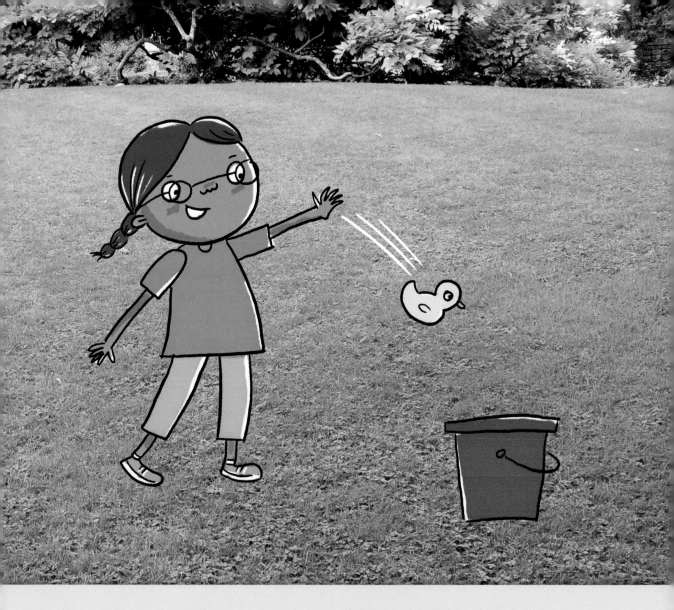

5 Get the duck in the red pot.

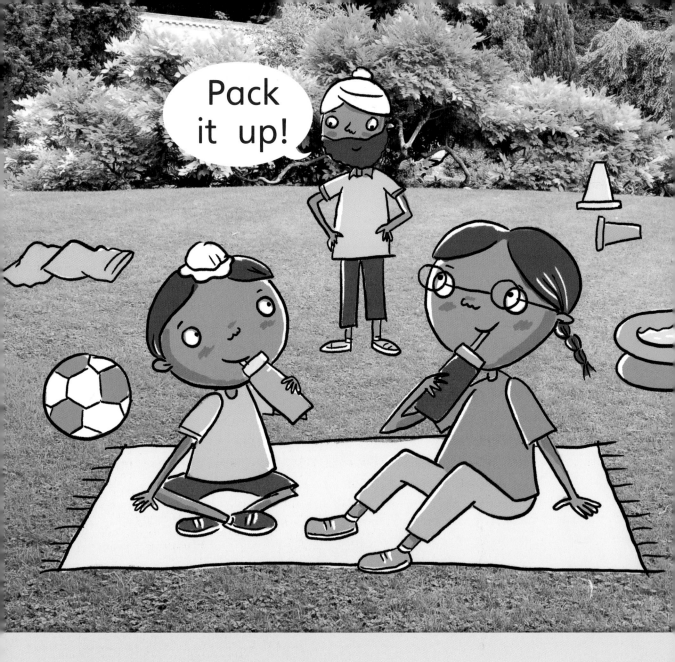

6 Sit and sip.